Pond Management Guide

North Carolina Wildlife Resources Commission
North Carolina Agricultural Extension Service

Contents

Pond Management Guide

North Carolina ponds are frequently fished by Tarheel anglers and represent a significant portion of the state's water resource. Properly managed ponds can provide excellent fishing opportunities to a large number of anglers at a reasonable cost. However, it takes careful planning and wise management to maintain high-quality fishing in a pond year after year.

To produce a good crop of fish every year, it is necessary to select the site carefully, construct the pond properly, maintain good water quality, and stock and harvest the pond correctly. Often the difference between a productive pond and an unproductive one is the ability of the owner to obtain sound pond management advice and carry out the recommended practices.

Before constructing a pond, determine your objectives and priorities for the pond. The best management strategy depends upon your objectives. Do you want the pond to produce trophy bass or large quantities of average-sized bass? Do you want big bream (bluegills) or channel catfish? Will the pond be used primarily for irrigation, livestock watering, waterfowl, or recreation? How heavily will the pond be fished? How much money can you devote to achieving your chosen objectives? You must answer these important questions during the initial planning stages so you can develop a proper management plan for the pond.

This publication presents the basic principles of managing recreational ponds and the requirements for producing and maintaining high-quality fishing in a pond. Some common mistakes in pond management and ways of solving pond problems are discussed. This information should allow you to develop and carry out a pond management plan that provides maximum benefits.

Perhaps the most important aspect of pond management is deciding where and how to build your pond. Many problems can be avoided if the pond is properly designed and constructed. The U.S. Soil Conservation Service (SCS) can provide excellent guidance. SCS representatives located in every county can advise on design surveys, site selection, drainage area, pond layouts, soil analysis, spillway construction, and cost estimation. To take advantage of these excellent free services, contact the SCS during the initial stages of pond planning.

There are two general types of ponds:

- Watershed or embankment ponds, which are formed by constructing a dam to collect stream or surface runoff,
- Excavated ponds, which are formed by digging down into the water table in an area that is relatively flat.

The type of pond that is best for your site will be determined to a great extent by the topography of the land and the principal use of the pond.

It is usually necessary to move more earth to construct an excavated pond than a watershed (embankment) pond. Watershed ponds, however, are more likely to have problems with muddy water, high siltation rates, rapid fluctuations in flow rates, aquatic weeds, temperature fluctuations, and wild fish invasions. Large watershed ponds can benefit from construction of a small settling pond immediately upstream to reduce turbidity, sedimentation, and weed problems in the large pond.

Permits

After choosing a site, contact a representative of the U.S. Army Corps of Engineers to make sure that the site is not located in a wetland area, especially if the pond is to be of the watershed type. Streams are considered wetland areas. If pond construction involves placing a dam across a stream or affects a wetland in other ways, you are required by law to obtain a 404 permit from the Corps of Engineers before starting construction.

Additional permits may also be required for certain types of watershed ponds. If the dam height will exceed 15 feet and impounded water volume (at the dam crest) will exceed 10 acre-feet, you are required to obtain two additional permits (one for construction and one for impoundment of water) from the North Carolina Department of Environmental Health and Natural Resources (EHNR), Dam Safety Division. The agency may also require that you prepare a sediment and erosion control plan to prevent excessive siltation in the stream being impounded during construction. To ensure that your pond will conform to all state laws, contact the nearest regional EHNR office before beginning construction.

The following sections present information that should be considered when designing and constructing a pond.

Drainage Area

An important factor in deciding where to build a pond is the nature of the surrounding watershed or drainage area. Generally, a pond built in pasture-land requires 5 to 20 acres of watershed per acre of pond, whereas a pond constructed in woodland requires 20 to 40 acres. If the drainage area is too large, it may be necessary to construct a diversion ditch to channel excess water around the pond. If the drainage area is insufficient, the pond will not fill adequately and will be subject to water-level fluctuations and vegetation problems.

Water Source and Quality

Potential water sources for a pond include surface runoff, streams, springs, and wells. Each source has advantages and disadvantages; the type chosen will depend to a large extent on where the pond is located. *Surface runoff* is rarely a source of disease or wild fish problems but leads to fluctuations in pond level during spring and fall. *Streams* are usually high in dissolved oxygen, but they also tend to fluctuate rapidly, are a source of silt, and are a potential source of diseases and wild fish invasions.

Springs are considered the most desirable water source because they have a constant temperature and flow rate, are very inexpensive to divert, are rarely a source of disease or wild fish problems, and are less likely to be affected by pollution. However, they may contain high concentrations of undesirable gases (hydrogen sulfide and carbon dioxide), and the high clarity of the water from most springs encourages vegetation problems. *Wells* offer good water quality and can be placed where convenient, but they are expensive to drill and operate.

It is also important to consider land uses within the watershed where the pond is located, as these may degrade the water quality. Runoff from cropland can increase the amount of sediment reaching the pond and may cause turbidity. It may also contain potentially toxic agricultural chemicals, as well as fertilizers that can cause algal blooms and resultant fish kills. Runoff from pastures and livestock holding areas is rich in nutrients (animal wastes) that can also cause algal blooms and fish kills. Residential, urban, and industrial runoff may contain substances (such as industrial waste, chemicals, oils, and sediment from construction activities) that can adversely affect a pond's water quality. When planning a pond, therefore, be sure to consider the quality of the water source and factors that may affect it.

Site Preparation

In constructing ponds of 3 acres or less to be used primarily for fishing, remove all brush, trees, and vegetation from the site before the pond is filled. If the pond is free of obstructions, it is easier to maintain the delicate balance between predator fish (largemouth bass) and their prey (sunfish), and it can be seined to remove excess sunfish if necessary. Some type of structure, such as trees or bushes, can be added to the pond later, if needed, to provide cover for small fish and to increase the production of aquatic insects for fish food. To prevent soil erosion, revegetate the dam and pond banks as soon as possible after construction has been completed. New ponds should be filled by early to mid-fall to coincide with the best period for stocking sunfish.

Size

The best fishing ponds have a surface area of at least 1 acre. Ponds of less than 1 acre are difficult to manage because the fish populations, especially largemouth bass, are easily overharvested. In addition, small, shallow ponds are susceptible to vegetation problems that usually result in overpopulation of sunfish. These problems ultimately result in stunted growth of both bass and sunfish. The fish populations in ponds of less than 1 acre are also adversely affected by drought. If you have a small pond and cannot afford to enlarge it, the best management tactic is to stock it with a single species of fish, such as channel catfish or hybrid sunfish, and begin a feeding program (discussed in a later section).

Depth

The average depth for a 1-acre fish pond should be between 6 and 8 feet with a maximum depth not greater than 10 to 12 feet. An average depth less than 6 feet greatly increases the probability of aquatic vegetation becoming established in the pond, and depths greater than 12 feet are not necessary for good fish production. Pond banks should be cut on a 3-to-1 slope and should be a minimum of 3 feet deep at the waterline before leveling off (Figure 1). This shape will help prevent the growth of nuisance aquatic vegetation and will also discourage muskrats.

Water Control Structure

An important feature that should be incorporated into the design of all fish ponds greater than 1 acre is a water control structure (drainpipe). A drainpipe enables you to drain the pond to make repairs, fix leaks, and control nuisance aquatic vegetation. It also makes it possible to treat and remove undesirable fish species chemically and to manage the fish population more effectively. In addition, a drainpipe that incorporates a bottom drawoff device (Figure 2)

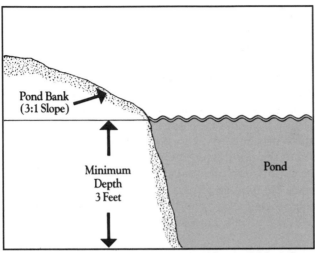

Figure 1. Slope of the pond bank at the water's edge.

ensures good water quality and reduces the chances of a fish kill by removing stagnant water from the bottom of the pond. Ponds tend to stratify in summer and winter, resulting in a bottom layer that is low in dissolved oxygen and may contain high concentrations of toxic gases (such as carbon dioxide, hydrogen sulfide, and ammonia).

Another important feature that you should incorporate is an emergency spillway. This structure is designed to prevent loss of the dam during periods of extremely high water by rerouting excess water through a low spot over or around the dam. To meet individual requirements, it is best to ask the Soil Conservation Service (SCS) to assist with this aspect of pond design.

Contacting the appropriate agency when first considering construction of a pond can prevent many costly mistakes.

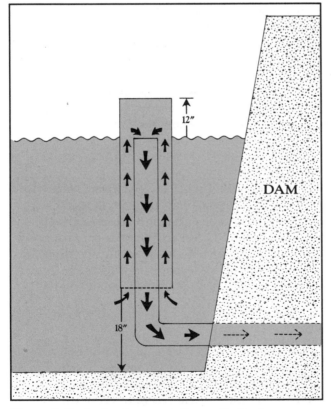

Figure 2. Drainpipe incorporating a device for drawing water from the bottom of the pond.

Prestocking Procedures

New Ponds. Plan construction so the pond is completed and filled by September or early October. Ponds filled in the summer may become contaminated with undesirable fish, which should be removed before stocking.

Existing Ponds. Restocking a pond usually requires eradicating existing fish populations (a process known as pond reclamation). Contact the North Carolina Wildlife Resources Commission to determine if reclamation is necessary; sometimes the problem may be solved by other means. Pond reclamation is often required when fish populations become unbalanced (for example, when there are too many sunfish and no bass) but may also be necessary if undesirable species such as crappies or bullheads are found in the pond. Undesirable fish populations are eliminated by using a fish toxicant called rotenone. Rotenone may be purchased from the Wildlife Resources Commission, and a Commission employee must be present when the chemical is applied. Follow these steps when reclaiming a pond with rotenone:

1. Plan the reclamation for August or September. The water is warm at this time, and rotenone will detoxify quickly. This will also allow time for the pond to refill by fall when sunfish are normally restocked.

2. Prepare the pond by lowering the water to its lowest level. This reduces the amount of rotenone needed and concentrates the fish in a smaller area, ensuring a complete kill. Close the overflow pipe and check daily for leaks so that treated water will not escape and kill fish downstream.

3. Contact the Wildlife Resources Commission to obtain rotenone. After treatment, most fish will die and come to the surface within 24 hours, although fish may continue to appear for several days. Rotenone is not approved by the Food and Drug Administration for human consumption, and therefore the poisoned fish should not be eaten by humans or livestock. Bury them to prevent odors and pest problems.

4. Allow at least 10 days for the rotenone to break down (detoxify) naturally. In warm water (65° to 70°F) the rotenone should be gone in approximately four days. The treated water should not be used for watering livestock for at least 10 days and should not be released from the pond for at least two weeks after application. Fish may be stocked two weeks after treatment.

Selecting the Proper Fish

Largemouth bass, bluegills, redear (or hybrid sunfish), and channel catfish are the only fish with which a pond should be stocked. Research has proven that various combinations of these fish produce the best pond fisheries. Stocking the pond with any other species of fish makes it difficult to manage, usually resulting in poor fishing and an unbalanced fish community. The following paragraphs briefly describe the desirable fish species and their characteristics to help you better understand fish populations.

Largemouth Bass. This species is recognized by its large mouth and dark stripes or blotches down its side (Figure 3). Young bass feed on microscopic animals (zooplankton) and insects until they are 2 inches long, when they start feeding on fish. Adult bass eat mostly fish, but they also eat large insects, frogs, and crayfish when available. Although their growth rate varies across North Carolina, most bass reach a harvestable size (12 inches) in 2 to 3 years when food is abundant. Bass spawn once a year, usually beginning in late March in eastern counties and as late as June in western counties.

Figure 3. Largemouth bass.

Bluegill. This species of fish, also called bream, is recognized by its small head and mouth and an irregular black spot located at the base of the soft dorsal (top) fin (Figure 4). Broad, dark vertical bands can sometimes be seen on the sides of the fish when it is in the water. Bluegills prefer to eat insects but they also sometimes feed on small fish. Their growth rate depends on the amount of food available and the number of fish in the pond. It usually takes three years to produce fish of harvestable size (5 inches long). Bluegills spawn frequently from May through October when the water temperature is higher than 80°F. Because they produce such large numbers of young fish, they are the primary food source for largemouth bass.

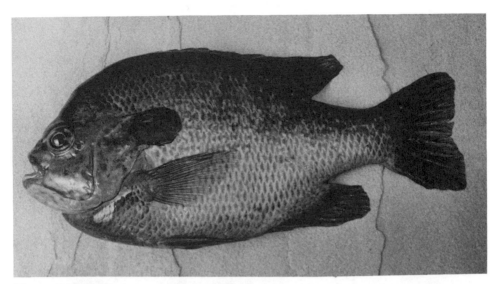

Figure 4. Bluegill.

Figure 5. Redear sunfish.

Redear Sunfish. Also known as the shellcracker, the redear sunfish has a small mouth and head and is shaped much like a bluegill (Figure 5). The opercular (cheek) tab of the redear is black with a red-orange border, and breeding males have a bright orange border. The redear is primarily a bottom feeder, eating mostly snails and insects. Its growth rate is similar to that of the bluegill, but redears typically reach a larger size because they are harder to catch. They are less prolific than bluegills and rarely become overpopulated.

Hybrid Sunfish. This fish is a cross of two different sunfish species, usually a bluegill and a green sunfish (Figure 6). The hybrid sunfish resembles the bluegill but has a much larger mouth. It is an active feeder and is generally easier to catch than other sunfish. Because of their voracious feeding activities, hybrid sunfish can reach a harvestable size (5 inches) in about two years. Hybrid sunfish spawning is limited because approximately 90 percent are males.

Figure 6. Hybrid sunfish.

Channel Catfish. This type of catfish can be recognized by its scaleless body, chin barbels (whiskers), dark spots scattered on the body, forked tail, and barbed spines on the dorsal and pectoral fins (Figure 7). Channel catfish will eat almost anything, but they prefer insects, small fish, and crayfish. They readily adapt to an artificial (pelleted) diet, which increases their growth rate. They are capable of spawning in ponds, but because of egg predation by

Figure 7. Channel catfish.

bluegills and fingerling predation by bass, very few young channel catfish
survive. Spawning success may be improved by placing 2-foot sections of
terra-cotta pipe (8 to 12 inches in diameter) perpendicular to the bank in 2 to 4
feet of water.

The above species are the *only* ones recommended for pond stocking.
Crappies, bullheads, and other sunfish species should not be stocked because
they tend to become overcrowded, resulting in populations that can be corrected only by pond reclamation.

Stocking Options

Except for supplementary stocking of hybrid sunfish or channel catfish, stocking a pond that already contains fish is normally not recommended. Before
stocking a new or reclaimed pond, be sure to contact the Wildlife Resources
Commission or the North Carolina Agricultural Extension Service for assistance in selecting a stocking regime best suited to your management plan for
the pond. Stocking the pond with the proper species and numbers of fish at the
proper time, combined with good management practices, is necessary to
maintain good fishing.

Sunfish fingerlings should be stocked in the fall, usually in October or No-
vember, so they can grow large enough to avoid predation by bass, which are
stocked the following June. The fish stocking combinations given in the accompanying tables usually produce a successful fishery. The stocking rates are
given as a general guide. In some cases the stocking rate should be altered,
depending upon the pond management plan, extent of fishing, water quality,
and other uses of the pond.

Option 1: Largemouth Bass and Sunfish Fingerlings in a 1-to-10 Ratio

Species	Number Per Acre		Size (inches)	When Stocked
	Fertilized	Unfertilized		
Bluegill	700	350	1 to 2	Oct. to Nov.
Redear sunfish	300	150	1 to 2	Oct. to Nov.
Channel catfish (optional)	100	50	2 to 4	Oct. to Nov.
Largemouth bass	100	50	2 to 4	The following June (after sunfish)

Option 1 is an economical and commonly recommended stocking plan for
establishing a fishery of largemouth bass and bluegills. However, harvesting
must usually be postponed at least two years for sunfish and three years for
bass. Supplementary stockings of channel catfish may be necessary; if so, 6- to

8-inch fingerlings should be stocked to reduce predation by bass. These rates should be used for ponds of 10 acres or less. Ponds larger than 10 acres should be stocked with 3,500 bluegill, 1,500 redear, 500 largemouth bass, and 500 channel catfish.

Option 2: Largemouth Bass and Sunfish Adults

Species	Number Per Acre	Size (inches)	When Stocked
Bluegill	70	3 to 5	April
Redear sunfish	30	3 to 5	April
Largemouth bass	20	8 to 14	April

Stocking adult fish (option 2) usually costs more than stocking fingerlings, but it will provide fishing sooner.

Ponds larger than 10 acres should be stocked with 700 bluegill, 300 redear sunfish, and 200 largemouth bass.

Option 3: Channel Catfish and Hybrid Sunfish Fingerlings

Species	Number Per Acre	Size (inches)	When Stocked
Channel catfish	100	2 to 4	June or July
Hybrid sunfish	300	1 to 2	June or July

Option 3 yields an excellent fishery for avid catfish and sunfish fishermen and is the best option for ponds of less than 1 acre. These fish grow quickly when fed a commercial fish diet. Since their reproductive potential is limited, both species should be restocked every two years at the original stocking rate.

Several commercial hatcheries provide fingerling fish for private ponds. A list of these hatcheries may be obtained from the Wildlife Resources Commission or the Agricultural Extension Service. It is advisable to contact several commercial facilities to obtain the best price and delivery arrangements.

Harvesting

Proper fish harvesting is one of the more important factors in pond management. You may fish the pond after the first year, although bass should not be harvested until after the third year or when they reach 12 to 14 inches in length. Overharvesting, particularly of bass, may easily occur when a pond is first opened to fishing, and it can ruin a good pond. The bass originally stocked must support the bass harvest for at least three to four years from the time of stocking.

Bass growth and subsequent harvesting rates are different for each pond. As a general rule, unfertilized ponds receiving runoff from agricultural lands can support a harvest of about 20 to 25 pounds of bass per acre each year. In excavated or infertile ponds, about 10 to 15 pounds per acre is a safe rate. These harvesting rates may be doubled if the management plan includes a fertilization program.

A 12- or 14-inch size limit for bass should be established. Generally, bass under 12 inches should not be harvested because they are very aggressive feeders and help maintain the proper population balance between bass and sunfish. Bass under 12 inches should be handled carefully before they are released.

Remember to spread the harvest throughout the fishing season. If too many adult bass are removed, particularly in the spring, the bluegills may become overcrowded. Keep a record and request others fishing the pond to record the number of bass caught and the number removed from the pond. When the annual quota is reached, fishing may continue but any bass caught should be released.

Good records should also be kept for the other fish caught, particularly channel catfish and hybrid sunfish. As a rule, these two species may be harvested at will. However, if large numbers are removed soon after fishing begins, restocking may become necessary earlier than anticipated.

Sunfish growth and harvesting rates are also different for each pond. As a general rule, you may remove at least 40 pounds of harvestable-size sunfish per acre annually from an unfertilized pond. This rate may be doubled for ponds with high basic fertility and those in which a fertilization program is used. Always harvest more sunfish, particularly bluegills, than bass. Attempt to harvest approximately 4 to 5 pounds of sunfish for each pound of bass per year. Sunfish are rarely overharvested, but underharvesting of sunfish is one of the most common causes of pond problems. When in doubt, it is better to keep a sunfish than throw it back.

Determining Balance

When is a fish population in balance? How can I determine if a balanced condition exists in my pond? These are two questions often asked by pond owners. Actually, a truly balanced condition never exists in a pond. Fish populations continually change and never reach the state of equilibrium, or general stability, referred to as balance. Fisheries biologists sometimes use the term to describe satisfactory relationships between the predator (bass) and prey (bluegill) populations of a pond. Generally, a balanced population must provide three things:

- Fish of harvestable size
- Annual reproduction
- A combination of fishes, including at least one predator species.

Unbalanced populations are those unable to produce annual crops of harvestable-size fish.

The two methods described in the accompanying table may be used to determine balance in a pond of largemouth bass and bluegills. The first method, using angler harvest information, is based on a correctly stocked bass-bluegill combination. The seine method, using a minnow seine 20 feet by 4 feet with 1/4-inch mesh, is effective during June and July in ponds containing a bass-bluegill population at least two years old. Sampling four or five shoreline locations around the pond should yield results in one of the population condition categories.

If the results from one or both of these methods indicate an overcrowded or undesirable condition, contact the Wildlife Resources Commission or the North Carolina Agricultural Extension Service for assistance. The fisheries biologist or Extension agent will usually recommend a corrective measure described for the following population conditions.

Overcrowded Bass. If bass populations are overcrowded, the situation can usually be corrected by harvesting the surplus bass. A Wildlife Resources Commission fisheries biologist or an Agricultural Extension agent can determine the total number or weight to be harvested, based upon pond size and degree of overcrowding.

Overcrowded Bluegills. This condition can occasionally be corrected by removing at least 100 pounds of sunfish per surface acre of pond. If no bass are present, restock the pond with 50 advanced (6- to 8-inch) bass fingerlings per acre. If overcrowding is not too severe, winter drawdown may correct the problem. Reducing water levels from December 1 to March 1 to approximately one-half the normal pond level concentrates the stunted sunfish, allowing bass to consume the surplus fish. If overcrowding persists, the pond should be drained, poisoned with rotenone (reclaimed), and restocked with the correct bass-to-bluegill ratio.

Undesirable Fish Population. Fish removal or drawdowns are rarely effective in eliminating populations of undesirable fish species. This problem usually requires pond reclamation and restocking to establish a successful bass-bluegill fishery.

Methods for Determining Pond Balance

I. Angler Method

Harvest Data	Population Condition
• Bluegills 6 inches and larger. Bass average from 1 to 2 pounds, although smaller and larger sizes also caught.	Balanced population.
• Bluegills average more than 1/3 pound. Bass average less than 1 pound and are in poor condition.	Unbalanced populations with bass overcrowded. (May be desirable if large sunfish are preferred.)
• Principally small bluegills, 3 to 5 inches long. Very few bass are caught, and those caught are larger than 2 pounds in size.	Unbalanced populations with bluegills overcrowded and stunted (May be desirable if trophy bass are the primary objective.)
• Small crappies, sunfish, bullheads, carp, suckers, or other undesirable fish of any size.	Undesirable fish population.

II. Seine Method

Fish Collected by Seining	Population Condition
• No young bass present. Many recently hatched bluegills. No or few 3- to 5-inch bluegills.	Unbalanced populations with bass overcrowded.
• No young bass present. No recently hatched bluegills. Many 3- to 5-inch bluegills.	Unbalanced population with bluegills overcrowded.
• Young bass present. Many recently hatched bluegills. Few 3- to 5-inch bluegills.	Balanced population.
• Young bass present. No recent hatch of bluegills. No 3- to 5-inch bluegills.	Unbalanced population. Bluegills absent.
• No game fish species present. Few to many carp, suckers, bullheads, shad, or other undesirable species.	Undesirable fish population.

Fertilization

As with land and crops, the fertility of the water determines the productivity of a pond. A more productive pond supports greater numbers of fish and sustains a larger harvest than a less productive pond. The addition of a pond fertilizer to the water stimulates the growth of microscopic plants (phytoplankton) and animals (zooplankton), which comprise the base of the food chain (Figure 8). These organisms are fed upon by insects and small fish, which provide forage for larger game fish. Ponds located in fertile watersheds may require little or no fertilization. Fertilization is also a method for preventing the growth of nuisance rooted vegetation by limiting light penetration to the bottom of the pond where plants become established.

Pond fertilization can, however, have negative side effects. Excessive fertilization can create noxious algal blooms. In addition, the decomposition of dead algae during summer months can cause low oxygen levels, which may cause fish kills during extended periods of cloudy weather.

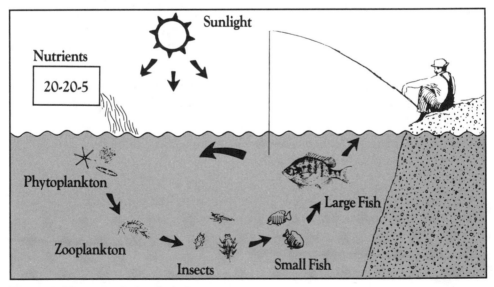

Figure 8. The aquatic food chain.

As a general guide, you can determine whether fertilizer is required by the water clarity. If a light-colored or shiny object, such as your hand or a small (6-inch) pie tin or lid can be seen clearly 18 inches under water, fertilizer is required.

Once begun, fertilization should be continued. Discontinuing fertilization will affect fish populations by reducing the food supply and encouraging the growth of aquatic vegetation. *It is better not to fertilize at all than to do so in a random manner.* Do not fertilize ponds that are not heavily fished or that have extensive shallow areas. *Do not apply fertilizer to ponds with weeds already present, as the fertilizer will promote weed growth and compound the problem.*

Before beginning a fertilization program, measure the pH and hardness of the water. Ponds with acidic or soft water may not respond to fertilization. The water chemistry can be analyzed by a Wildlife Resources Commission biologist. The application of lime is discussed in the following section.

Begin fertilization in spring when water temperatures reach 60°F. Because ponds differ greatly, the number of applications of fertilizer needed per year cannot be predicted. Usually two to three applications, spaced two weeks apart, are required for a plankton bloom (greenish color) to develop. After the initial application, apply additional fertilizer as needed to maintain a bloom until late summer or fall.

Fertilization may not be effective in ponds with high flow rates, muddy water, or stained water. If a bloom does not develop after the third application, consult a biologist.

Several types of granular and liquid pond fertilizers are available. Most agricultural fertilizers do not have the best combination of nutrients for ponds. They include components that are unnecessary and may stimulate an undesirable type of algae. The following types of fertilizers and application rates are recommended:

Type	Application Rate
10-34-0 (liquid)	1 gallon per acre
20-20-5 (granular)	40 pounds per surface acre
8-8-2 (granular)	100 pounds per surface acre

Generally, liquid fertilizer is preferred because it goes directly into solution and is more economical. Because liquid fertilizer is heavier than water, it should always be mixed with water (one part of fertilizer to five parts of water) before application. It is best to siphon or pour diluted liquid fertilizer from a container while moving over the pond in a boat. If this method cannot be used, the diluted fertilizer can be sprayed or splashed around the edge of the pond, although this sometimes encourages the growth of undesirable algae and weeds. Do not use liquid fertilizers having a petroleum base.

Granular fertilizer should be spread on a platform 12 to 18 inches below the surface (Figure 9) so that it will be dissolved and dispersed by water currents. The platform should be located 10 to 15 feet from the bank. In watershed ponds it should be placed in the upper two-thirds of the pond, away from the drainpipe. For ponds of 3 acres or less, a platform with 9 square feet of surface area is adequate, whereas ponds of more than 3 acres require 3 1/2 square feet per acre. Ponds up to 10 acres can be fertilized with one platform.

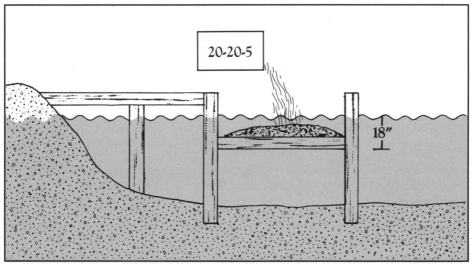

Figure 9. Platform for dispersion of granular fertilizer.

Granular fertilizer can also be mixed with water and spread around the pond from the bank or by boat into water 5 feet deep or less. However, this type of fertilizer is most effective when it is not applied directly to the pond bottom because chemicals in pond mud can bind the nutrients, and fertilizer on the pond bottom can encourage weed growth.

Liming

Some ponds benefit from the occasional addition of lime. Ponds with very soft, acidic water (less than 20 parts per million total alkalinity) may not respond to fertilization without liming. Ponds with acidic waters (water having a low pH value) are common in some areas of the coastal plain. Fishing will be poor if the pH is below 6.0. A pH value between 6.5 and 9.0 is considered optimum for fish ponds.

For ponds under construction, the soil pH can be measured by the North Carolina Department of Agriculture Soil Testing Laboratory. Collect soil from areas throughout the pond, mix it, and allow it to dry. Then place the sample in a shipping box available from your county Agricultural Extension Service agent and mail it. Identify the sample as a pond sample. Lime, if required, can be spread over the bottom of the pond and disked in before the land is flooded.

For existing ponds, the pH can be measured by the North Carolina Soil Testing Laboratory (using the procedure described above), by Wildlife Resources Commission biologists, or by using litmus paper available at swimming pool supply dealers and drugstores. About 1 ton of lime per acre is required to raise the pH one unit. The lime should be distributed as evenly as possible over the entire pond. A common method for applying lime is to shovel it from a plywood platform while moving around the pond in a boat. The best time to apply lime is in the late fall or early winter preceding a spring fertilization program. If this cannot be done, apply lime at least two weeks before fertilization. A typical pond requires retreatment with lime every 3 to 4 years, although ponds with high rates of inflow and outflow require more frequent applications.

Hydrated or builder's lime (calcium hydroxide) is generally not recommended, as it is caustic and has the potential to increase pH too much, killing the fish. If fish are not present or if agricultural lime is not readily available, hydrated lime can be applied carefully at the rate of 50 pounds per surface acre. Retreatment every few months is often required with hydrated lime.

Supplemental Feeding

Supplemental feeding can be used to increase the growth of fish and harvesting rates of ponds. Feeding is not necessary for most ponds, as an adequate quantity of natural food organisms (insects, worms, and crustaceans) are present to support fish populations. In small, infertile ponds, supplemental feeding may be preferable to fertilization for increasing productivity. Feeding is not recommended for fertilized ponds.

Bluegills and channel catfish will readily take feed, whereas bass usually do not. However, some commercial hatcheries sell "trained" bass that have been conditioned to consume artificial feed.

Feed only between spring and fall when the water temperature exceeds 65°F. Stop feeding if the water temperature is greater than 90°F, as fish will generally not feed at higher temperatures. It is best to place the feed in the pond daily at several locations. Feed only the amount that the fish consume in about 10 to 15 minutes and no more than 10 pounds per acre per day. Excessive feeding can cause fish kills because the decomposition of uneaten feed depletes the oxygen supply. Discontinue feeding if the fish stop accepting the feed. Automatic and demand feeders are commercially available.

Be sure to continue a feeding program once you have started it. If feeding is discontinued while the fish are still accepting feed, there may be more fish than the natural food supply can support, resulting in stunted fish of poor quality. Occasional feeding will do little to increase fish growth.

Several commercial feed preparations are available in either floating or sinking varieties. Although more expensive, floating feed makes it possible to observe the extent and duration of feeding. Floating feed can be placed in floating plastic rings that prevent the pellets from washing ashore. Moldy feed should not be used, as it can be toxic to fish.

Habitat Improvement

Various devices can be used in ponds to concentrate fish and improve fishing. Best results are obtained in ponds that are devoid of natural cover such as stumps, tree tops, and aquatic vegetation. The devices should be located within casting distance of the shoreline or piers. Floats can be used to mark the location of the devices.

Automobile Tires. Tires can be used to construct a satisfactory permanent structure, but they must be prepared properly. First slit them to allow them to sink and prevent them from floating around the pond. Then tie them together with polypropylene rope to keep them in position. Adding one or two cement blocks to the bundle will help stabilize it. The higher the structure is above the bottom of the pond, the more cover it will afford. Pyramid-shaped bundles are commonly used. Tires tossed in a pond at random will either wash ashore or silt in and provide no fishery benefits. Tires can be covered with brush to further increase their attractiveness to fish.

Brush Piles. Any available woody material can be used to make a brush pile. Again, the more vertical the pile, the better. Cedar and discarded Christmas trees can be set into cement blocks, secured with polypropylene rope, and set upright on the pond bottom. Several trees located together work better than single trees. Brush piles generally have to be replaced every few years.

Stake Beds. Any type of wooden stakes can be driven into the pond bottom or nailed to a weighted frame and sunk. The stakes should be placed 6 to 8 inches apart, and the bed should cover an area of about 200 square feet. The stakes should extend from the shoreline into water that is from 6 to 8 feet deep. The tops of the stakes should extend out of the water so they can be located easily.

Fish Kills

Fish die from a variety of natural causes. Observing a few dead fish in a pond is not uncommon and is no reason for concern unless it continues for several days. When fish die in large numbers, however, there is reason for concern.

A common cause of fish kills is oxygen depletion. This condition usually occurs during summer in very fertile ponds as a result of pond turnover or the die-off of an algal bloom. During hot weather most ponds have a layer of water near the bottom that contains little or no dissolved oxygen. When high winds or cold rain cause this water to mix with the upper pond water, oxygen levels often drop low enough to kill fish. Oxygen depletion also occurs when dead algae or other plants decay in the pond after herbicides have been applied to control weeds.

Preventing oxygen depletion is difficult, but the following suggestions may help:

- Follow the prescribed fertilization guidelines and **do not overfertilize!**

- **Do not** allow animal waste to enter the pond.

- **Do not** treat aquatic weeds with herbicides during the summer months, except under the supervision of a professional such as a fisheries biologist or Extension agent. If a herbicide application is necessary, treat no more than one-fourth to one-third of the pond at a time to prevent oxygen depletion and a resulting fish kill.

- During extremely hot weather, check your pond regularly at sunrise for signs of stressed fish. If fish are observed at the pond's surface gulping for air, stop feeding the fish and aerate the pond as soon as possible. Oxygen can be added to the pond by circulating the water with an irrigation pump or by running an outboard motor around in the pond. Commercial aerators do an excellent job of aeration. The paddlewheel type is especially effective, as it moves a large volume of water.

Although fish kills caused by pesticides, herbicides, or other chemicals are not as common as those caused by oxygen depletion, some do occur. If you suspect that your fish were killed by a toxic substance, try to determine what chemical was involved and call the Division of Environmental Management in Raleigh, North Carolina (919-733-2314).

Be very careful when spraying herbicides or other pesticides, as many are highly toxic to fish. *Always read and follow label instructions!*

Fish kills resulting from low pH (acidic water) are even less common than chemical kills. Usually pH kills occur when heavy rains wash tannin (an acidic substance found in leaves) from wooded areas. Low pH can be increased easily by applying agricultural limestone. The amount of lime required can be determined by sending samples of the mud from the pond bottom to the North Carolina Department of Agriculture Soil Analysis Laboratory for analysis. (See the earlier section on liming procedures.) Contact your county Agricultural Extension Service office for assistance in sending soil samples.

Fish kills caused by diseases usually occur when fish are already stressed by poor water quality or overcrowding. In most situations little can be done once a disease strikes except wait for it to run its course and see what is left. Here again, prevention is the key: fish the pond properly, maintain good water quality, and watch for signs of problems such as poor fish growth, thin fish, and excessive numbers of small fish.

Poor Fishing

Most complaints about poor fishing stem from crowded or stunted bream (bluegill) populations. The best way to prevent this problem is to fish the pond properly. Correcting an unbalanced fish population is a lot more trouble than keeping it in balance from the start. If a fish population becomes unbalanced with too many small bream, it may be possible to correct the problem by stocking 25 to 50 largemouth bass (8 to 12 inches long) per acre. This solution may be prohibitively expensive, however, as bass in this size range are costly. Often the easiest and least expensive way of correcting the balance is to reclaim the pond and restock with fingerlings at the proper ratios.

Sometimes poor fishing can result from competition of gamefish with undesirable fish such as wild sunfish, shiners, bullheads, and crappies. These fish may enter the pond via feeder streams or be purposely stocked by anglers with good intentions. Again, prevention is much easier than the cure. When building a new impoundment, make sure that all wild fish are eliminated before stocking the pond with hatchery fish. Also, do not place wild fish in the pond or allow minnows to be used as bait.

Aquatic Weeds

Aquatic weeds often cause serious problems in ponds, interfering with fishing, boating, swimming, and irrigation. In addition, when vegetation is dense, bream often become overcrowded and stunted because the weeds prevent bass from adequately reducing their numbers. Extremely dense growths of filamentous algae and submerged weeds may also cause fish kills as a result of nighttime oxygen depletion. It is generally better to keep your pond clear of aquatic weeds.

Weeds that root to the bottom or begin forming on the bottom are usually a problem only in ponds that are shallow or have shallow areas (water less than 24 inches deep). Anytime sunlight can penetrate to the pond bottom, rooted aquatic weeds and filamentous algae may become established. Once established, many weeds have the ability to spread to deeper water.

Problems with planktonic algae and floating weeds, such as duckweed, usually develop in very fertile ponds. Ponds that receive runoff from livestock operations or other nutrient-rich areas are prime candidates for duckweed and algal problems.

The following methods have proven effective in North Carolina for controlling aquatic vegetation.

Winter Drawdown. Reducing the surface area of a pond by one-third to one-half from mid-November to the first of March helps control many submerged rooted aquatic plants by exposing them to drying and freezing. A side benefit in bass-bluegill ponds is improved fish population balance resulting from increased predation of bass on bluegills forced out of cover. Unfortunately, some weed species, such as hydrilla, cannot be controlled by winter drawdown because they produce tubers or other overwintering reproductive structures. Winter drawdown is not recommended in ponds of less than 1 acre.

Manual Weed Removal. Removing the plants by methods such as pulling, raking, or chaining works best on small patches of plants that are rooted in shallow water. Manual removal is most effective if performed in late spring or early summer before the plants form seeds. Be sure to dispose of the vegetation properly, especially alligator weed, which may root and grow on dry land.

Chemical Treatment. Weeds can be killed by treating the pond with one of the herbicides labeled for aquatic use. To determine which herbicide to use, ask an Agricultural Extension agent to identify the weeds. Unfortunately, herbicides only treat the symptoms and do very little to cure the problem. Weeds frequently return soon after treatment if no action is taken to deepen the pond or eliminate the nutrient source.

Triploid Grass Carp. These vigorous, fast growing, reproductively sterile, herbivorous fish can be used to control unwanted aquatic vegetation under certain conditions. They are an effective biological control agent for submerged weeds such as hydrilla, chara, elodea, widgeongrass, bladderwort, fanwort, coontail, pondweed (Potamogeton), naiads, and parrotfeather. They provide partial control of duckweed, eurasian watermilfoil, variable leaf milfoil, and some types of algae, but they generally are not very effective in controlling eelgrass, smartweed, American lotus, yellow waterlily, fragrant waterlily, maidencane, dollarweed, alligatorweed, torpedograss, and cattails. Grass carp grow large and provide effective control for 10 years or longer.

In their diploid (reproductively fertile) form, grass carp may damage valuable native vegetation and displace native fishes. Consequently, only grass carp that have been genetically manipulated to make them triploid (and therefore sterile) are allowed. A permit must be obtained from the Wildlife Resources Commission to release grass carp into any body of water in North Carolina. If you want a permit to stock triploid grass carp, obtain an application by calling or writing to:

N.C. Wildlife Resources Commission
Division of Boating and Inland Fisheries
512 N. Salisbury St., Room 458
Raleigh, NC 27611
Telephone (919) 733-3633

Pond Deepening. Deepening all areas of the pond to a minimum of 24 inches will reduce weed infestations. Most pond owners use this method as a last resort, but for shallow ponds it is often the only lasting solution.

Fertilization. Weed problems can sometimes be prevented through fertilization. Fertilizer is often applied to weed-free ponds to stimulate the growth of planktonic algae, which darken the water and prevent sunlight from reaching the pond bottom, thus preventing the germination of most aquatic weeds.

Fertilizer should be applied only to ponds that are clear of weeds. Applying fertilizer to ponds with established weeds will usually increase the growth of those weeds.

Other Pond Problems

Muskrats. These burrowing animals often cause pond banks to collapse and dams to leak. Keeping the pond edge mowed and controlling emergent vegetation will discourage muskrats from taking up residence. Once established, however, these rodents are best controlled by trapping. If you do not want to trap them yourself, it is usually easy to find a local fur trapper to do the job. Muskrats should be trapped during the regular trapping season by a licensed trapper unless a depredation permit has been obtained from a Wildlife Enforcement Officer.

Beavers. Occasionally, beavers take up residence in ponds. When they do, they usually cause considerable damage. They often block drain pipes and dam spillways, and they dig dens in the pond banks and dams. As with muskrats, trapping is the best way to remove these animals.

Turtles. These slow-moving creatures are primarily scavengers and do not harm fish populations. They may, however, eat fish off a stringer, or in the case of snapping turtles, eat a few ducks. Snapping turtles can be caught on large set hooks baited with scrap meat or fish, or they can be baited into wire baskets. Other types of turtles that like to bask in the sun can be caught in sink box traps (Figure 10).

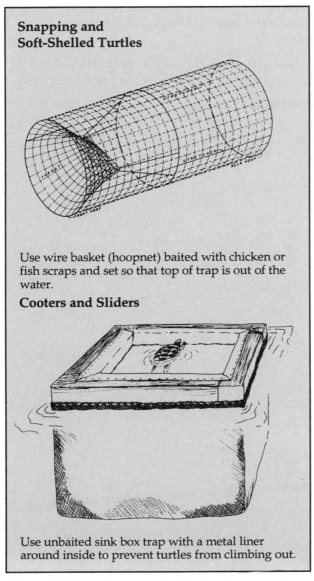

Snapping and Soft-Shelled Turtles

Use wire basket (hoopnet) baited with chicken or fish scraps and set so that top of trap is out of the water.

Cooters and Sliders

Use unbaited sink box trap with a metal liner around inside to prevent turtles from climbing out.

Figure 10. Traps for removing turtles from ponds.

Snakes. Most snakes seen in and around ponds are nonpoisonous water snakes. The only problem they present is that they may scare pond owners and fishermen. The best way to control snakes is to keep the pond banks mowed, thus eliminating their hiding places.

Muddy Water. The first step in clearing a muddy pond is to eliminate the source of the turbidity. Common causes of muddy water are runoff from non-vegetated acreage in the watershed, livestock wading in the pond, or some undesirable fish species (such as common carp or bullheads) stirring up the bottom of the pond. After the source of the turbidity has been eliminated, the water will usually clear naturally, but this may take from several weeks to several months, depending on the soil type in the watershed. Some ponds may not clear naturally because their water chemistry keeps the clay particles from settling out.

The following treatments have proven successful in clearing muddy ponds:

- Spread 7 to 10 bales of hay and 40 pounds of superphosphate per acre over the surface of the pond. Do not use this treatment during the summer months because of the danger of depleting the oxygen.

- Apply 100 pounds of cottonseed meal and 40 pounds of super phosphate per surface acre.

- Apply 300 to 500 pounds of gypsum (land plaster) per surface acre. The gypsum should be finely ground and spread over the pond's surface.

In mild cases a standard fertilization program may effectively clear the pond.

Sources of Additional Information 5

Further information on pond planning, design, and construction is available from the U.S. Soil Conservation Service. Contact the local district conservationist or the U.S. Soil Conservation Service, State Conservationist's Office, Raleigh, NC 27611.

The North Carolina Wildlife Resources Commission can provide additional information on pond stocking, pond management, reclamation, and grass carp permits. Contact your district fisheries biologist or the North Carolina Wildlife Resources Commission, 512 N. Salisbury St., Raleigh, NC 27611.

Information on pond stocking, pond management, and aquatic weed control is also available from the North Carolina Agricultural Extension Service. Contact your county Extension office.

Information on application rates, effectiveness, and water-use restrictions for aquatic herbicides may also be found in the *North Carolina Agricultural Chemicals Manual,* available at county extension offices or by writing to Agricultural Chemicals Manual, Campus Box 7603, North Carolina State University, Raleigh, NC 27695-7603.

Permit information and requirements for pond construction that may affect streams or wetland areas can be obtained from the Department of the Army, Wilmington District, Corps of Engineers, P. O. Box 1890, Wilmington, NC 28402-1890.

Information on dam safety and permit requirements is available from the North Carolina Department of Environmental Health and Natural Resources, Dam Safety Division, 512 N. Salisbury St., Raleigh, NC 27611.

Edited by
J. A. Rice, Extension Fisheries Specialist
North Carolina Agricultural Extension Service

R. L. Noble, Professor of Zoology and Forestry
North Carolina State University

F. T. McBride, Program Manager
North Carolina Wildlife Resources Commission

Contributing authors
K. W. Ashley, R. L. Curry, F. T. McBride, and K. L. Nelson,
Fisheries Biologists
North Carolina Wildlife Resources Commission

Figure 10 courtesy of the Nebraska Cooperative Extension Service.
15,000 copies of this publication were printed at a cost of $6,336 or 42 cents per copy.

Published by

THE NORTH CAROLINA WILDLIFE RESOURCES COMMISSION
and
THE NORTH CAROLINA AGRICULTURAL EXTENSION SERVICE

North Carolina State University at Raleigh, North Carolina Agricultural and Technical State University at Greensboro, and the U.S. Department of Agriculture, cooperating. State University Station, Raleigh, N.C., Paul E. Dew, Interim Director. Distributed in furtherance of the Acts of Congress of May 8 and June 30, 1914. The North Carolina Agricultural Extension Service offers its programs to all eligible persons regardless of race, color, or national origin and is an equal opportunity employer.